UNIT 14
Run for Cover

INTER·
Active
Mathematics
Activities & Investigations

GLENCOE
McGraw-Hill

New York, New York   Columbus, Ohio   Mission Hills, California   Peoria, Illinois

Send all inquiries to:
Glencoe/McGraw-Hill
936 Eastwind Drive
Westerville, OH 43081

ISBN: 0-02-824562-8 (Student Resource Book)
ISBN: 0-02-824163-0 (Teacher's Edition)

2 3 4 5 6 7 8 9 10 VH 01 00 99 98 97 96 95 94

CONTENTS

UNIT 14

RUN FOR COVER

SURFACE AREA AND VOLUME

Interdisciplinary Applications

DAVID FOSTER

"The national goal is to develop mathematical power for all students. My vision for learning mathematics includes a student-oriented classroom culture, where students are taking charge of their own learning and are actively engaged in a curriculum that reflects today's world, not the mathematics of 150 years ago."

**Former Teaching Consultant
Middle Grades Mathematics
Renaissance**
Morgan Hill, California
Author of Units 1, 2, 5, 6, 7, 8, 10, 11, 13, 15,16, 17, and 18

David Foster received his B.A. in mathematics from San Diego State University and has taken graduate courses in computer science at San Jose State University. He has taught mathematics and computer science for nineteen years at the middle school, high school, and college level. Mr. Foster is a founding member of the California Mathematics Project Advisory Committee and was Co-Director of the Santa Clara Valley Mathematics Project. Most recently, he has taken the position of Consulting Author for Glencoe Publishing. Mr. Foster is a member of many professional organizations including the National Council of Teachers of Mathematics and regularly conducts in-service workshops for teachers. He is also the author of a book on computer science.

SANDIE GILLIAM

"Many students only see mathematics as isolated number facts and formulas to memorize. By using this program, which incorporates the mathematics into a context of large, real-life units tied together with literature, science, and history, the middle school student can find meaning in the mathematics."

**Mathematics Teacher
San Lorenzo Valley High School
Felton, California**
Co-author of Unit 14

Sandie Gilliam received her B.A. from San Jose State University and is a mentor teacher and instructor for the Monterey Bay Area Mathematics Project. She was a semi-finalist for the Presidential Award for Excellence in the Teaching of Mathematics in the state of California. Ms. Gilliam has served as a consultant for the California Department of Education and many local school districts and county offices of education. She is a member of the National Council of Teachers of Mathematics and is a frequent speaker at conferences and teacher in-service workshops. Ms. Gilliam was a writer and consultant for Glencoe's *Investigating Mathematics: An Interactive Approach.*

JACK PRICE

"This program is designed to help students become mathematically powerful as they develop problem-solving skills and self-reliance, as well as the ability to work well with others. At the same time, they will strengthen their basic skills and be exposed to new and exciting ideas in mathematics."

**Co-Director, Center for Science
and Mathematics Education**
**California State Polytechnic
University**
Pomona, California
Author of Unit 3

Jack Price received his B.A. from Eastern Michigan University and his Doctorate in Mathematics Education from Wayne State University. Dr. Price has been active in mathematics education for over 40 years, 38 of those years at grades K through 12. In his current position, he teaches mathematics and methods courses for preservice teachers and consults with school districts on curriculum change. He is president of the National Council of Teachers of Mathematics, is a frequent speaker at professional conferences, conducts many teacher in-service workshops, and is an author of numerous mathematics instructional materials.

INTERACTIVE MATHEMATICS AUTHORS

KAY McCLAIN

"Building conceptual understanding in mathematics challenges us to re-define what it means to know and do mathematics. This program was developed to allow teachers to become facilitators of learning while students explore and investigate mathematics — strengthening their understanding and stimulating interest."

Kay McClain

Doctoral Candidate
George Peabody College
Vanderbilt University
Nashville, Tennessee
Author of Unit 9, Co-author of Unit 14

BARNEY MARTINEZ

"Students learn mathematics best when their teacher enables them to become actively involved in worthwhile mathematical investigations. Students should be encouraged to interact with each other. Then, through their collaborative efforts, students build their own understanding of mathematics."

Barney Martinez

Mathematics Teacher
Jefferson High School
Daly City, California
Co-Author of Unit 12

LINDA DRITSAS

"This program is designed to encourage students to be creative and inventive, while gaining mathematical power. Open-ended situations and investigations provide the setting that allows students to work at varying depths, while nurturing their natural curiosity to learn."

Linda Dritsas

Mathematics Coordinator
Fresno Unified School District
Fresno, California
Author of Unit 4, Co-author of Unit 12

Kay McClain received her B.A. from Auburn University and her Educational Specialist degree from the University of Montevallo in Montevallo, Alabama. While a teacher at Mountain Brook Middle School in Birmingham, she received the Presidential Award for Excellence in the Teaching of Mathematics in the state of Alabama. Ms. McClain is a Woodrow Wilson fellow and a member of the National Council of Teachers of Mathematics. She regularly conducts teacher in-service workshops and is a frequent speaker at local, state, and national mathematics education conferences. She is also an author of middle school mathematics instructional materials.

Barney Martinez received his B.S. in mathematics from The University of San Francisco and is an instructor of pre-service mathematics teachers at the College of Notre Dame in Belmont, California. Mr. Martinez currently serves on the Mathematics Development Team of the California Department of Education and the Pursuing Excellence Revision Advisory Committee. He is a member of the National Council of Teachers of Mathematics and is very active as a speaker and workshop leader at professional development conferences.

Linda Dritsas received her B.A. and M.A. from California State University at Fresno. She taught middle school mathematics for many years and, for two years, taught mathematics at California State University at Fresno. Ms. Dritsas has been the Central Section President of the California Mathematics Council and is a member of the National Council of Teachers of Mathematics and the Association for Supervision and Curriculum Development. She frequently conducts mathematics teacher in-service workshops and is an author of numerous mathematics instructional materials, including those for middle school students and teachers.

CONTRIBUTORS INTERACTIVE MATHEMATICS

Each of the Consultants read all 18 units while each Reviewer read one unit. The Consultants and Reviewers gave suggestions for improving the Student Resource Books, Teacher's Editions, Cooperative Group Cards, Posters, and Transparencies. The Writers wrote the Student Diversity Strategies that appear in the Teacher's Edition.

CONSULTANTS

Dr. Judith Jacobs, *Units 1-18*
Director, Center for Science and Mathematics Education
California State Polytechnic University
Pomona, California

Dr. Cleo M. Meek, *Units 1-18*
Mathematics Consultant, Retired
North Carolina Dept. of Public Instruction
Raleigh, North Carolina

Beatrice Moore-Harris,
Units 1-18
College Board Equity 2000 Site Coordinator
Fort Worth Independent School District
Fort Worth, Texas

Deborah J. Murphy, *Units 1-18*
Mathematics Teacher
Killingsworth Jr. High School,
ABC Unified School District
Cerritos, California

Javier Solorzano, *Units 1-18*
Mathematics Teacher
South El Monte High School
South El Monte, California

WRITERS

Student Diversity Teacher's Edition

Dr. Gilbert J. Cuevas
Professor of Mathematics Education
University of Miami
Coral Gables, Florida

Sally C. Mayberry, *Ed.D.*
Assistant Professor Mathematics/Science Education
St. Thomas University
Miami, Florida

REVIEWERS

John W. Anson, *Unit 11*
Mathematics Teacher
Arroyo Seco Junior High School
Valencia, California

Laura Beckwith, *Unit 13*
Mathematics Department Chairperson
William James Middle School
Fort Worth, Texas

Betsy C. Blume, *Unit 6*
Vice Principal/ Director of Curriculum
Valleyview Middle School
Denville, New Jersey

James F. Bohan, *Unit 11*
Mathematics K-12 Program Coordinator
Manheim Township School District
Lancaster, Pennsylvania

Dr. Carol Fry Bohlin, *Unit 14*
Director, San Joaquin Valley Mathematics Project
Associate Professor, Mathematics Education
California State University, Fresno
Fresno, California

David S. Bradley, *Unit 9*
Mathematics Teacher/Department Chairperson
Jefferson Jr. High
Kearns, Utah

Dr. Diane Briars, *Unit 9*
Mathematics Specialist
Pittsburgh City Schools
Pittsburgh, Pennsylvania

INTERACTIVE MATHEMATICS CONTRIBUTORS

Jackie Britton, *Unit 18*
Mathematics Teacher
V. W. Miller Intermediate
Pasadena, Texas

Sybil Y. Brown, *Unit 8*
Mathematics Teacher
Franklin Alternative Middle
School
Columbus, Ohio

Blanche Smith Brownley, *Unit 18*
Supervising Director of
Mathematics (Acting)
District of Columbia Public
Schools
Washington, D.C.

Bruce A. Camblin, *Unit 7*
Mathematics Teacher
Weld School District 6
Greeley, Colorado

Cleo Campbell, *Unit 15*
Coordinator of Mathematics,
K-12
Anne Arundel County
Public Schools
Annapolis, Maryland

Savas Carabases, *Unit 13*
Mathematics Supervisor
Camden City School District
Camden City, New Jersey

W. Karla Castello, *Unit 6*
Mathematics Teacher
Yerba Buena High School
San Jose, California

Diane M. Chase, *Unit 16*
Mathematics Teacher/
Department Chairperson
Pacific Jr. High School
Vancouver, Washington

Dr. Phyllis Zweig Chinn, *Unit 9*
Professor of Mathematics
Humboldt State University
Arcata, California

Nancy W. Crowther, *Unit 17*
Mathematics Teacher
Sandy Springs Middle School
Atlanta, Georgia

Regina F. Cullen, *Unit 13*
Supervisor of Mathematics
West Essex Regional Schools
North Caldwell, New Jersey

Sara J. Danielson, *Unit 17*
Mathematics Teacher
Albany Middle School
Albany, California

Lorna Denman, *Unit 10*
Mathematics Teacher
Sunny Brae Middle School
Arcata, California

Richard F. Dube, *Unit 4*
Mathematics Supervisor
Taunton High School
Taunton, Massachusetts

Mary J. Dubsky, *Unit 1*
Mathematics Curriculum
Specialist
Baltimore City Public Schools
Baltimore, Maryland

Dr. Leo Edwards, *Unit 5*
Director, Mathematics/
Science Education Center
Fayetteville State University
Fayetteville, North Carolina

Connie Fairbanks, *Unit 7*
Mathematics Teacher
South Whittier Intermediate
School
Whittier, California

Ana Marina C. Gomezgil, *Unit 15*
District Translator/Interpreter
Sweetwater Union
High School District
Chula Vista, California

Sandy R. Guerra, *Unit 9*
Mathematics Teacher
Harry H. Rogers Middle
School
San Antonio, Texas

Rick Hall, *Unit 4*
Curriculum Coordinator
San Bernardino County
Superintendent of Schools
San Bernardino, California

Carolyn Hansen, *Unit 14*
Instructional Specialist
Williamsville Central Schools
Williamsville, New York

Jenny Hembree, *Unit 8*
Mathematics Teacher
Shelby Co. East Middle
School
Shelbyville, Kentucky

Susan Hertz, *Unit 16*
Mathematics Teacher
Paul Revere Middle School
Houston, Texas

Janet L. Hollister, *Unit 5*
Mathematics Teacher
LaCumbre Middle School
Santa Barbara, California

Dorothy Nachtigall Hren, *Unit 12*
Mathematics Teacher/
Department Chairperson
Northside Middle School
Norfolk, Virginia

Grace Hutchings, *Unit 3*
Mathematics Teacher
Parkman Middle School
Woodland Hills, California

Lyle D. Jensen, *Unit 18*
Mathematics Teacher
Albright Middle School
Villa Park, Illinois

Robert R. Jones, *Unit 7*
Chief Consultant,
Mathematics, Retired
North Carolina Department
of Public Instruction
Raleigh, North Carolina

Mary Kay Karl, *Unit 3*
Mathematics Coordinator
Community Consolidated
School District 54
Schaumburg, Illinois

Janet King, *Unit 14*
Mathematics Teacher
North Gulfport Junior High
Gulfport, Mississippi

Franca Koeller, *Unit 17*
Mathematics Mentor Teacher
Arroyo Seco Junior High
School
Valencia, California

Louis La Mastro, *Unit 2*
Mathematics/Computer
Science Teacher
North Bergen High School
North Bergen, New Jersey

Patrick Lamberti, *Unit 6*
Supervisor of Mathematics
Toms River Schools
Toms River, New Jersey

Dr. Betty Larkin, *Unit 14*
Mathematics Coordinator
K - 12
Lee County School District
Fort Myers, Florida

Ann Lawrence, *Unit 1*
Mathematics
Teacher/Department
Coordinator
Mountain Brook Jr. High
School
Mountain Brook, Alabama

Catherine Louise Marascalco,
Unit 3
Mathematics Teacher
Southaven Elementary
School
Southaven, Mississippi

Dr. Hannah Masterson, *Unit 10*
Mathematics Specialist
Suffolk Board of
Cooperative Education
Dix Hills, New York

Betty Monroe Nelson, *Unit 8*
Mathematics Teacher
Blackburn Middle School
Jackson, Mississippi

Dale R. Oliver, *Unit 2*
Assistant Professor of
Mathematics
Humboldt State University
Arcata, California

Carol A. Pudlin, *Unit 4*
Mathematics Teacher/
Consultant
Griffiths Middle School
Downey, California

Diane Duggento Sawyer,
Unit 15
Mathematics Chairperson
Exeter Area Junior High
Exeter, New Hampshire

Donald W. Scheuer, Jr., *Unit 12*
Mathematics Department
Chairperson
Abington Junior High
Abington, Pennsylvania

Linda S. Shippey, *Unit 8*
Mathematics Teacher
Bondy Intermediate School
Pasadena, Texas

Barbara Smith, *Unit 1*
Mathematics Supervisor,
K-12
Unionville-Chadds Ford
School District
Kennett Square, Pennsylvania

Stephanie Z. Smith, *Unit 14*
Project Assistant
University of Wisconsin-
Madison
Madison, Wisconsin

Dora M. Swart, *Unit 11*
Mathematics Teacher
W. F. West High School
Chehalis, Washington

Ciro J. Tacinelli, Sr., *Unit 8*
Curriculum Director:
Mathematics
Hamden Public Schools
Hamden, Connecticut

Kathy L. Terwelp, *Unit 12*
K-8 Mathematics Supervisor
Summit Public Schools
Summit, New Jersey

Marty Terzieff, *Unit 18*
Secondary Math Curriculum
Chairperson
Mead Junior High School
Mead, Washington

Linda L. Walker, *Unit 18*
Mathematics Teacher
Cobb Middle School
Tallahassee, Florida

RUN FOR COVER

Looking Ahead

In this unit, you will see how mathematics can be used to answer questions about surface area and volume. You will experience:

▶ discovering formulas for the area of geometric figures

▶ finding the volume of solid figures

▶ exploring surface area by building a parachute

▶ examining the relationship between surface area and volume in objects of varying shape and size

Did You Ever Wonder?

What do mathematics and changing relationships have to do with each other? Turn the page and see how Minnie Carachure of Selma, California, combines the two!

Teens in the News

Featuring: Minerva "Minnie" Carachure
Age: 18
Hometown: Selma, California
Career Goal: Civil engineering and politics
Interests: Working with people

Minerva "Minnie" Carachure grew up in a family of six children. When Minnie was barely ten years old, her mother died. Minnie's father tried to raise the children by himself. However, in 1989, Minnie and her brothers and sisters were placed in foster homes. Since then, Minnie has been in ten foster homes!

All of these changes were hard on Minnie. She was very angry with the world. Minnie's anger and the choices she made got her expelled from high school her freshman year.

Minnie was moved to a foster home in Selma, California, where she entered Selma High School. She met two friends at Selma High who helped her change her life. Her friends didn't believe in peer pressure. They told Minnie that every choice she made was hers and hers alone.

Now Minnie chooses to spend her time in fun, productive activities. She was elected Student Body President her senior year. She belongs to the Mathematics, Engineering, and Science Achievement Club and serves as a math tutor and peer counselor to other teens. As a member of Students for the Ethical Treatment of Animals, Minnie helps out at the local animal shelter. She even finds time to work as a grocery store cashier.

The one thing that has been constant in Minnie's life is *change*. Minnie has decided that *good change* is a wonderful thing!

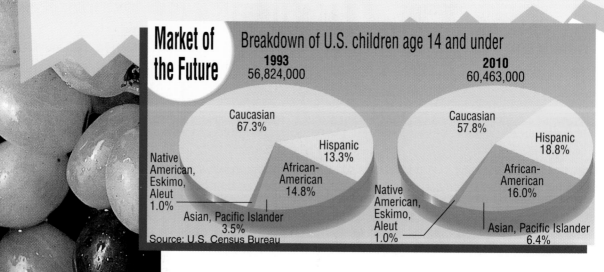

Market of the Future

Breakdown of U.S. children age 14 and under

1993
56,824,000

- Caucasian 67.3%
- Hispanic 13.3%
- African-American 14.8%
- Native American, Eskimo, Aleut 1.0%
- Asian, Pacific Islander 3.5%

2010
60,463,000

- Caucasian 57.8%
- Hispanic 18.8%
- African-American 16.0%
- Native American, Eskimo, Aleut 1.0%
- Asian, Pacific Islander 6.4%

Source: U.S. Census Bureau

Team Project

Measure Up

As a member of the Future Farmers of America, Minnie found out that she lives in the raisin capital of the world. Hundreds of acres of land in Selma, California produce thousands of bushels of raisins.

An *acre* is a unit of measure of land area equal to 43,560 square feet. A *bushel* is a unit of measure of capacity equal to 8 gallons. Do research and compile a list of units of area and capacity in the metric and customary systems. Try to find how the units were named and when they were first used.

AD 100 Construction of The Great Pyramid of Cholula in Mexico begins.

1806 Construction begins on the National Road, the first road engineered and built by the U.S. government.

1964 Joseph Montoya becomes the first Mexican-American elected to the U.S. Senate.

1986 Engineering marvel Eurotunnel, a 31-mile, 3-tunnel undersea transportation system under the English Channel is started.

A.D.100   1900

400 BC   1800   1952   2000

312 BC Italian civil engineers begin construction of the 162-mile Via Appia, Europe's first conventional road.

1904 Civil engineers start work on the Panama Canal.

Cesar Chavez begins organizing farm workers, an action which lead to the powerful United Farm Workers Union.

1976 Birth of Minnie Carachure

For more information

If you would like more information about scholarship possibilities, contact:

National Hispanic Scholarship Fund
P.O. Box 728
Novato, California 94948

You can learn more about the math Minnie uses by completing the following activities in this unit.

Setting the Scene

MATHEMATICS TOOLKIT

Many professions require the use of tools. This mathematical toolkit includes tools you may find useful as you study this unit.

You may remember reading the book James and the Giant Peach by Roald Dahl. It is about a boy named James who was sent to live with his two aunts after his parents were killed. In the story, a tiny old man appears to James and gives him a bag of small, magic, green things about which he says, "Whoever they meet first, be it bug, insect, animal, or tree,...will be the one who gets the full power of their magic!" By accident, James drops the bag near a peach tree and, as a result, a peach receives the full power of the magic green things. Take time to read this toolkit and remember the questions that are asked and answered by the characters.

Narrator: Nigel, Carmelita, Moon, and Simone are students at Great Plains Middle School. They have just read the book *James and the Giant Peach* to a group of 4th graders at the nearby elementary school. They are discussing some of the mathematical curiosities of the book with their math teacher, Mr. Hernandez.

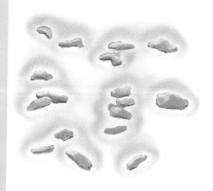

Mr. Hernandez: What kinds of things did you discover while reading *James and the Giant Peach* to the children?

Nigel: I don't know if I made any discoveries, but I did have some questions.

Mr. Hernandez: What kinds of questions?

Nigel: Well, for example, in Chapter 6, when James' aunts were looking at the peach they said, "The thing really *is* growing! It's nearly twice as big already!" Did they mean twice as much to eat, twice the diameter, or twice the surface area?

Carmelita: Well, I think it means that there was twice as much to eat. That's the same as twice the diameter, isn't it?

Moon: I don't know, Carmelita. Isn't the diameter the distance across the peach through the center, Mr. H?

Mr. Hernandez: Yes, it is.

Moon: Well, if you doubled the diameter, you would double the distance around the peach. So that means there would be twice the surface area.

Simone: I don't think that's right either, Moon.

You're trying to use a circle to describe something that is close to a sphere in shape. A sphere is a 3-dimensional object. I don't think the rules work that way.

Mr. Hernandez: That's a good point, Simone. Sometimes questions like this don't have one right answer. They might have meant twice as much to eat or twice the diameter. Only the author knows what he meant. While we're on the subject, Simone, what did you find interesting about the story?

Simone: In Chapter 7, it says that James—well, let me read it: "He could see the peach swelling larger and larger as clearly as if it were a balloon being blown up. In half a minute, it was the size of a melon!" I was wondering how many times its size it would have to grow for it to be the size of a melon. I mean, how many peaches would fit inside a melon?

Carmelita: That depends on what kind of melon it was. The volume of a cantaloupe is different from the volume of a watermelon.

Moon: I found something in Chapter 7, too. It says, "Soon it was the size of a small car, and reached half-way to the ground." Then a little later, it says, "Bigger and bigger grew the peach, bigger and bigger and bigger. Then at last, when it had become nearly as tall as the tree that it was growing on, as tall and wide, in fact, as a small house, the bottom part of it gently touched the ground—and there it rested." Okay. How tall was the tree? How big could the peach have been? I mean, this stuff is unbelievable!

Mr. Hernandez: What does volume have to do with it, Carmelita?

Carmelita: Volume describes the size of the inside of something. We could find the volume of a melon, and then divide it by the volume of a peach to find out how many peaches would fit inside a melon.

Mr. Hernandez: Good thinking! What about you, Moon? Did you have questions about the story?

Mr. Hernandez: Don't forget, Moon, that this book is fiction.

Moon: I know that, Mr. H. But how big *could* the peach have been?

Mr. Hernandez: Well, how big is a small car? And how big is a small house?

These are the kinds of questions you would need to answer in order to know how big the peach was.

Simone: What kinds of measurements would we use?

Nigel: I think we would need to know the surface areas of a small car and a small house.

Carmelita: But Nigel, the surface area wouldn't help. That only tells us how much material would be needed to say, paint the car or the house. I think we need to know the area. That would tell us how much of the ground it covered.

Moon: But what do we care about the ground it covered? We are comparing the sizes of the peach, a small car, and a small house, right? I think we need to know the volume of all three.

Mr. Hernandez: Okay, you guys. Why don't you work together to figure it out?

Stop the Script!
Estimate the sizes of a small car and a small house. Then use these measurements to estimate the size of the peach at both stages of its growth.

Narrator: The next day, the students report their findings to Mr. Hernandez.

Mr. Hernandez: So, what did you find out?

Moon: We found out that volume was the best measurement to use to describe the size of the peach—just like I said! The volume of a small car turned out to be about 6 cubic meters and the volume of a small house turned out to be about 370 cubic meters. That would be a huge peach!

Carmelita: Well, Moon, since you know so much, I've got a question for you. In Chapter 16, I read a part that really stumped me. You try and figure it out.

Moon: Okay, shoot.

Carmelita: It's talking about what happened after the centipede chewed through the peach stem and the peach started rolling down the hill. "The peach was now only a hundred yards away from the cliff—now fifty—now twenty—now ten—now five—and when it reached the edge of the cliff it seemed to leap up into the sky and hang there suspended for a few seconds, still turning over and over in the air... Then it began to fall... Down... Down... Down... SMACK! It hit the water with a colossal splash and sank like a stone. But a few seconds later, up it came again, and this time, up it stayed, floating serenely upon the surface of the water." How is that possible? Shouldn't the peach have sunk? Was it because it was magic?

Moon: Well,...uh...I'm not sure.

Mr. Hernandez: For tonight's homework...

All: (moans and groans)

Mr. Hernandez: ...I'd like you to do a little research on something called Archimedes' principle. That's spelled A-R-C-H-I-M-E-D-E-S, but it's pronounced Ark-uh-meed-ees. Write a one-page report about this principle for tomorrow's class. Have a nice day!

Narrator: The next day, the students discuss their reports in class.

Mr. Hernandez: Nigel, what did you find out?

Mr. Hernandez: Does anybody else know why the peach didn't sink?

Simone: Maybe it was wearing a life jacket! (laughter)

Mr. Hernandez: You're not too far off, Simone. What makes a person float when they're wearing a life jacket?

Simone: Oh, I don't know. I was only kidding!

Carmelita: Doesn't it have something to do with weight? I mean, a rock will sink, but those pool toys that you blow up won't.

Nigel: That's right! Maybe whatever it is just has to be heavy enough.

Moon: I don't know. After all, a person is pretty heavy, but some people can float.

Nigel: Well, Archimedes was a Greek philosopher who lived in the third century B.C. His principle says that the buoyant force on an object in a fluid is equal to the weight of the fluid displaced by the object.

Carmelita: I found the same information. But what does that mean?

Simone: I know! My mom explained it to me. It means that an object will float when it displaces enough fluid to equal its weight.

In other words, if the density of the object is greater than the fluid it's in, the object will sink. If not, it will float.

Mr. Hernandez: So how does that answer your question, Carmelita?

Carmelita: Now I know that the density of the peach was not as great as the density of the water that the peach was in. That means that the peach weighed less than an equal amount of water. So, it floated.

Mr. Hernandez: Excellent reasoning, Carmelita. Well, I guess everyone else has chosen a part of the book to discuss, so let me tell you the part of *James and the Giant Peach* that I found the most interesting. It's in Chapter 18. Poor old Earthworm was worried that they would all starve. "'If this peach is not going to sink,' the Earthworm was saying, 'and if we are not going to be drowned, then every one of us is going to starve to death instead.'

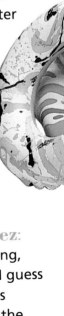

Do you realize that we haven't had a thing to eat since yesterday morning?' ...James took a deep, slow breath. 'Can't you realize,' he said patiently,' that we have enough food here to last us for weeks and weeks?'" I like this part because I *love* peaches! How long do you think it would take James, eating normal-sized meals, to eat the peach, assuming that, by this time, the peach was the size of a small house?

Stop the Script!

Estimate the number of normal-sized meals that you could eat from the peach.

Simone: Since we already found that the volume of a small house was about 370 cubic meters, we can find the volume of a normal-sized meal and divide that into the volume of the house. Isn't that right, Mr. Hernandez?

Mr. Hernandez: That's one way to go about it, Simone.

Nigel: I think a normal-sized meal is about the size of a square dinner plate measuring, oh, about 25 centimeters on a side. If the food is say, 3 centimeters high, the volume of that meal would be 1,875 cubic centimeters. But how many cubic meters is that?

Moon: Boy, is this complicated!

Mr. Hernandez: Not really, Moon. Remember that 1 cubic meter = 100 centimeters × 100 centimeters × 100 centimeters. Take a look at this model.

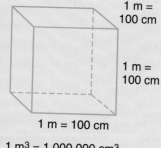

1 m = 100 cm

1 m = 100 cm

1 m = 100 cm

$1 \text{ m}^3 = 1,000,000 \text{ cm}^3$

Moon: Oh yeah! I'd forgotten about that. 1 cubic meter = 1,000,000 cubic centimeters. Therefore, 1,875 cubic centimeters = 1,875 ÷ 1,000,000 or 0.001875 cubic meter.

Carmelita: So that means James could eat 370 ÷ 0.001875 normal-sized meals of peach. When I punch that into my calculator, I get 197,333.33. That's a lot of meals!

Mr. Hernandez: Don't forget, class, that the pit takes up a significant amount of space.

Simone: I don't know, Mr. Hernandez. Say we ignore the pit for a minute. If James ate three meals a day, that's about 180 *years* worth of meals! Even if we consider the pit, he'd still have—what—100 years worth of meals?

Nigel: You know, I love peaches too. But I think that would be one peach pie too many!

This concludes the Mathematics Toolkit. It included many mathematical tools for you to use throughout the unit. As you work through this unit, you should use these tools to help you solve problems. You may want to explain how to use these mathematical tools in your journal. Or you may want to create a toolkit notebook to add mathematical tools you discover throughout this unit.

May I Take Your Order?

The **surface area** of an object is the number of square units needed to cover the object. The **volume** of an object is the number of cubic units needed to fill the interior space of the object.

Cut out the models on Blackline Masters 14-PA and 14-PB. Fold and tape them together to form rectangular prisms, cubes, and cylinders.

Using the materials your teacher has provided, arrange the models in order from least to greatest surface area. Then arrange the models from least to greatest volume.

When your group is finished, write down as many conclusions as you can draw from your experiment.

Make a poster that reflects what you have learned. Be prepared to explain your technique for ordering the models.

In This Area,...

You can find the areas of certain figures by looking at examples and then finding a pattern.

The rectangles below have areas measuring 24 square units and 35 square units.

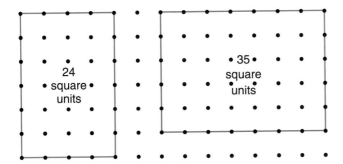

Can you determine a method for finding the area of a rectangle?

Work with your group to determine methods for finding the areas of rectangles, right triangles, acute triangles, obtuse triangles, parallelograms, and trapezoids. Then write a one-page report explaining how to find the areas of these figures.

You can use the methods for finding area that you developed in this activity to find the surface areas of 3-dimensional objects. How much area do you need to cover to paint the barn shown below? Assume that there are four windows on two sides of the barn and a pair of doors and one window on each end of the barn. Be sure to consider the surface areas of all doors and windows. Then write a one-page analysis that describes your method.

Cast Your Net
How Many Nets?

MENU
station
A

1 **U**sing a cube and some construction paper, design and cut out all of the different possible nets that will completely cover (but not overlap) the cube. Share your nets within your group. Then glue or tape your nets to a sheet of posterboard.

2 **F**ind a strategy for finding all of the patterns for the nets to cover the cube.

3 **H**ow many 1-centimeter cubes would fill your cube?

4 **T**he number of centimeter cubes that would fill the cube is the volume of the cube. Find a method that you could use to calculate the volume. Explain your method.

5 **S**ummarize your findings in writing.

Fill the Nets

1 **C**hoose a container from the ones you brought in. Then design and cut out all of the different possible nets that will completely cover (but not overlap) the solid.

2 **F**ind a strategy for finding all of the patterns for the nets to cover the solid, without using trial and error.

3 **H**ow many 1-centimeter cubes would fill each container?

4 **T**he number of centimeter cubes that would fill each solid is the volume of the solid. Find a method that you could use to calculate the volume. Explain your method.

5 **S**ummarize your findings in writing.

Upstairs, Downstairs

Use construction paper to design one net to cover each solid shown below. Then find the surface area and volume of each solid figure.

MENU
station
C

1 **3** cubes

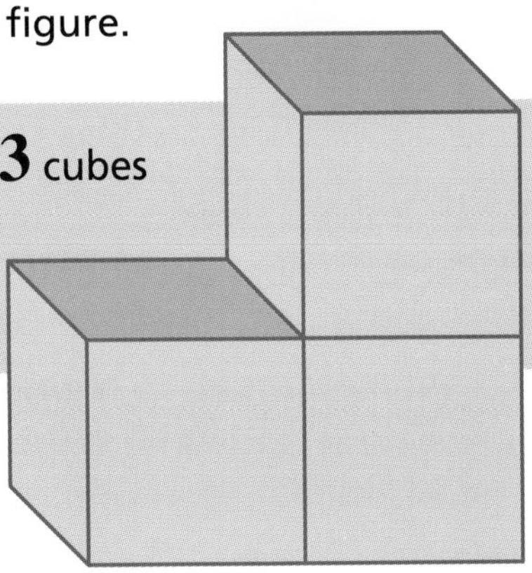

2 **4** cubes

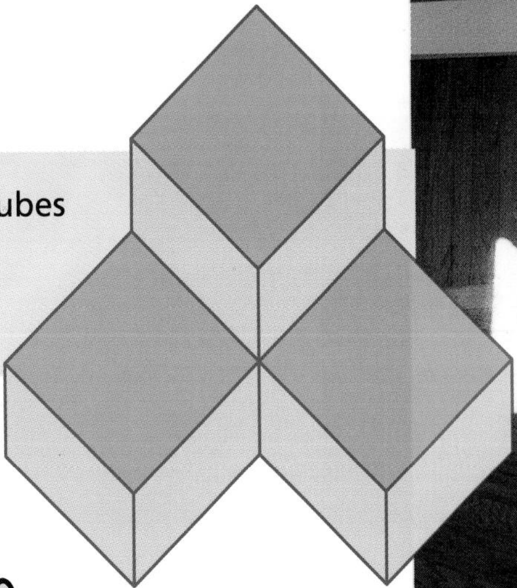

3 **S**ummarize your findings in writing.

Prisms

You can use other measures to determine the size of a container.

1 **C**hoose a container from the ones you brought in. Using the measuring tools and your container, estimate how many of each measuring tool the container will hold.

2 **S**ketch your container on a sheet of paper. Use a centimeter ruler to measure each side and write these measurements on your sketch.

3 **F**ind the volume of your container in cubic centimeters.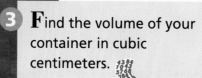

4 **U**se the measuring tool to fill your container. Then find the conversion factor of your measuring tool. For example:

1 (my measuring tool) = _____ cubic centimeters

5 **U**se this conversion factor to verify the volume you found in #3.

6 **S**ummarize your findings in writing.

Cylinders

You can use other measures to determine the size of a container.

1 Choose a container from the ones you brought in. Using the measuring tools and your container, estimate how many of each measuring tool the container will hold.

2 Sketch your container on a sheet of paper. Use a centimeter ruler to measure the cylinder and write these measurements on your sketch.

3 Find the volume of your container in cubic centimeters.

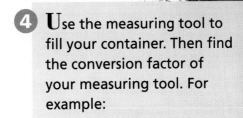

4 Use the measuring tool to fill your container. Then find the conversion factor of your measuring tool. For example:

1 (my measuring tool) = _____ cubic centimeters

5 Use this conversion factor to verify the volume you found in #3.

6 Summarize your findings in writing.

JUST HANGIN' AROUND

The United States Armed Services are in need of new parachutes. They are looking for a parachute that has good hang time—that is, it stays in the air for a relatively long time—but doesn't cost much money. Both of these factors are very important. They are asking your company to submit a parachute for testing. The government contract will be awarded to the company with the greatest hang time for the money.

Your task is to construct a parachute with the materials provided. At the end of the designated time, you will be asked to submit your parachute for an official test flight. (You should test your parachute yourselves first.) You will not be able to use any additional materials, but you can cut the ones you have been provided (except for the paper clip).

It is very important that you remember that both hang time and surface area will be considered. The government is looking for the best combination; that is, the longest hang time and the least surface area.

Keep a record of the steps you follow while constructing your parachute. Explain how you arrived at your parachute size and shape.

Float On

1. Fill a graduated cylinder with water so that it won't overflow when you add a cube. Write down the amount of water in the cylinder.

2. Place the cube in the water. What happened? Why do you think it happened?

3. With the tip of a pencil, make sure that the cube is submerged, but very little of the pencil is. Write down the measure of the water level. How much different is this measure? Why is this measure different?

4. Draw conclusions based on your experiment. Verify your conclusions by using two other different-sized cubes.

5. Find an irregularly-shaped object either inside or outside the classroom and find its volume by using this method.

After verifying your conclusions, write a summary of your experiment. Be sure that your summary answers the following questions.

- Given a container of water, what will be the effect of putting a cube into the water?
- Does the size of the cube affect anything?
- How could a container of water be used to find the volume of a cube?

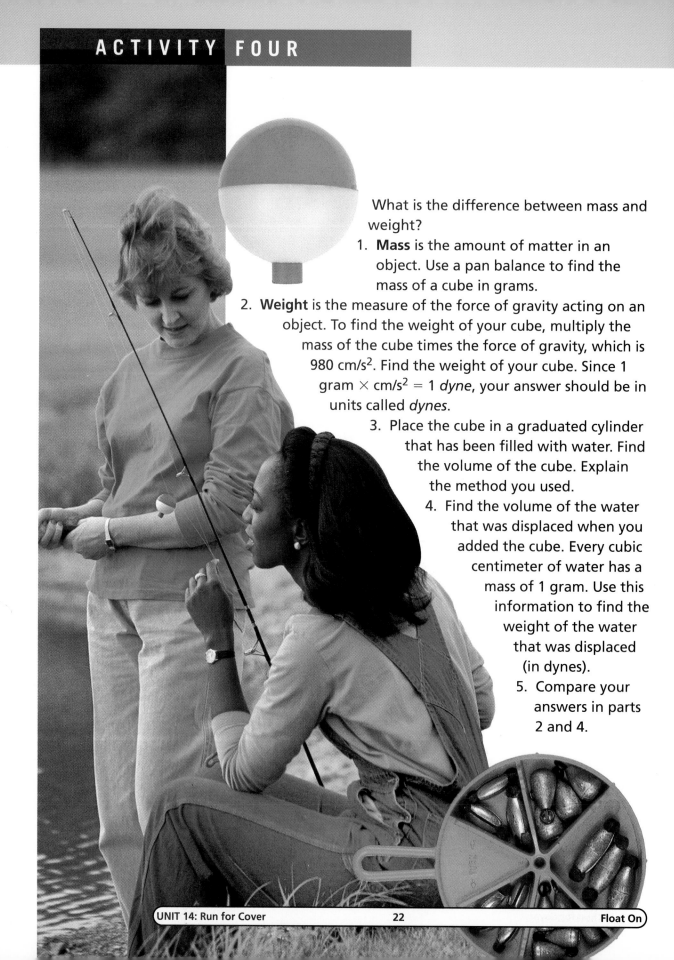

ACTIVITY FOUR

What is the difference between mass and weight?

1. **Mass** is the amount of matter in an object. Use a pan balance to find the mass of a cube in grams.

2. **Weight** is the measure of the force of gravity acting on an object. To find the weight of your cube, multiply the mass of the cube times the force of gravity, which is 980 cm/s^2. Find the weight of your cube. Since 1 gram $\times$ cm/s^2 = 1 *dyne*, your answer should be in units called *dynes*.

3. Place the cube in a graduated cylinder that has been filled with water. Find the volume of the cube. Explain the method you used.

4. Find the volume of the water that was displaced when you added the cube. Every cubic centimeter of water has a mass of 1 gram. Use this information to find the weight of the water that was displaced (in dynes).

5. Compare your answers in parts 2 and 4.

Why do some things float and others sink? Find an object that will sink in water.

1. Use the pan balance to find the mass of the object.

2. Calculate the weight of the object.

3. Fill a container with water. Add the object and calculate the amount of water that is displaced when the object is submerged.

4. Find the weight of the displaced water.

5. Compare your answers in parts 2 and 4.

6. How do you predict whether an object will float or sink? Explain your reasoning.

7. Find an object. Use mathematics to predict whether it will float or sink. Then test your conclusion.

Archimedes' Principle

In the third century B.C., Archimedes, a Greek philosopher, proposed an explanation for why objects float or sink. Archimedes' principle states that the buoyant force on an object in a fluid is equal to the weight of the fluid displaced by the object.

That means that an object will float when it displaces enough fluid to equal its weight. A life jacket is lightweight compared to water since it displaces much more water than it weighs. Therefore, you float more easily.

If the density of an object is greater than the fluid it is in, the object will sink. If the density of an object is less than the density of the fluid, the object will float. What happens if their densities are exactly equal?

Submarines pump water into and out of chambers in order to regulate the depth at which they operate. How does Archimedes' principle apply to this situation?

Cool It!

The Social Club at Great Plains Middle School has planned a picnic. They want to take along an ice chest filled with soft drinks. Carmelita has offered to get an ice chest and fill it with drinks and ice. Moon asks her if she will use cubes of ice or one block of ice. Carmelita responds that she hasn't really thought about it.

Nigel says that the block will take up more space. Simone argues that it will take the same space. Moon says that the block is better. Who is correct?

Carmelita has room in her ice chest for a block of ice that is 10 inches by 10 inches by 10 inches and she will still have plenty of room for soft drinks. But remember, she could fill the same space with ice cubes.

Help the students keep cool! Decide if they should take the block of ice or the ice cubes, which each measure 1 inch by 1 inch by 1 inch. Write a statement that reflects your opinion and be prepared to defend it to your classmates.

You may use cubes to help you visualize the problem. A drawing may also be helpful.

Extend the problem by answering the following. If you had a block of ice measuring 10 inches by 10 inches by 10 inches, how could you cut it to maintain the volume, but increase the original surface area by one third?

Paint the Cube Red

Masaki has a cube that is 4 inches long on each side. He paints the cube red and then cuts the cube into smaller cubes that measure 1 inch on each side.

- How many of the smaller cubes does Masaki now have?

   - How many of the smaller cubes have exactly three sides painted red?

   - How many of the smaller cubes have exactly two sides painted red?

   - How many of the smaller cubes have exactly one side painted red?

      - How many of the smaller cubes have no sides painted red?

      - How could Masaki paint the original cube so that he would have exactly 27 cubes with exactly one side painted red?

Cutting Corners

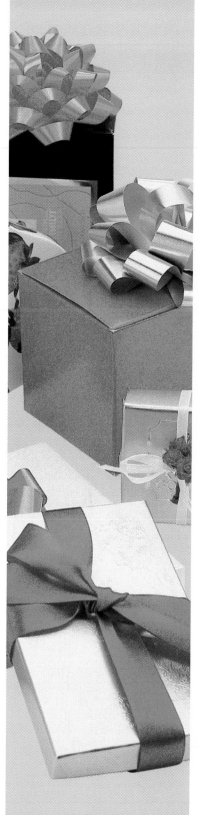

The Choc Full Chocolate Company is designing boxes to be used in selling their candies. The company is in the process of trying to determine which size would be best. One of the employees has suggested that they take a piece of cardboard 20 centimeters wide by 20 centimeters long, cut off the corners, fold it up, and make a box. The manager thought this was a great idea and sent an order to the local box company.

The box company was faced with a dilemma—they didn't know how much to cut off each corner. When they called Choc Full, the manager replied, "We don't want to cut corners! Make a box that will hold the most candy!"

You are an employee of the box company. You have been assigned the task of determining the dimensions of the box for the Choc Full Chocolate Company. Use the paper, scissors, and tape that have been provided to experiment with the boxes.

After you have determined a solution to the box problem, tape your box to the chart paper and list the dimensions. Be prepared to discuss how you determined the size and shape of your box in class.

Debriefing Guide

- What are the dimensions of the box with the greatest volume?
- How did you arrive at that conclusion?
- Would this be the best box? Why or why not?
- What other factors would you need to consider in making your decision?
- What factors would the Choc Full Chocolate Company need to consider in selecting the best box?
- Would the box with the greatest volume necessarily hold the most candies? Why or why not?
- What conclusions can you draw?

Using a Spreadsheet

COMPUTER investigation

Many companies use computer programs to help run their businesses more efficiently. One application program that is often used is called a **spreadsheet**. A spreadsheet is a computer program that is specially designed to create charts by doing many calculations. Let's investigate how a spreadsheet could be used to solve the box problem for The Choc Full Chocolate Company.

The sample headings below could be used in the spreadsheet program.

Length of Side of Square Cut Off	Length of Box	Width of Box	Height of Box	Volume of Box

Suppose we tell the computer the length of the side of the square that we will remove from each of the four corners of the cardboard. Let's investigate how we might tell the computer to calculate each of the numbers in the remaining columns. Examine the chart below.

Length of Side of Square Cut Off	Length of Box	Width of Box	Height of Box	Volume of Box
1 cm	18 cm	18 cm	1 cm	324 cm^3
2 cm	16 cm	16 cm	2 cm	512 cm^3
3 cm	14 cm	14 cm	3 cm	588 cm^3

Do you see a pattern developing? Use this pattern to write a formula to calculate a value for each column. Write a statement to explain the process you used.

IT'S A GAS!

Your company distributes gasoline to local gas stations and service stations. You have tankers that haul the gasoline and fill the buried storage tanks at each station. In the past several months, your company has been delivering gas to about fifty new dealers. Unfortunately, they are not familiar with your company and have been calling to complain about being cheated. One station owner said that the level in his tank dropped one fourth of the way and he had not used one fourth of the supposed volume.

Your customer service office tried to explain that since the tanks are cylinders and are buried on their side, a one-fourth drop in the level does not correspond to the usage of one fourth of the gasoline. As a result, station managers are requesting that they receive a stick that has been calibrated to indicate exactly how much gas remains in the tank at any one time.

Your research and development team has been asked to investigate the problem. Upper management would like for you to develop a stick that can be used to indicate what percentage of the tank is full. You want to be able to place the stick in the tank, read where the gasoline registers on the stick, and then determine how much gas remains in the tank. Remember, the tank is resting on its side. You should attack the problem assuming that the diameter of the tank is 1 meter and that the tank is 3 meters long.

Research this problem and be prepared to present a solution at the next board meeting. In addition to developing the stick, prepare a detailed report as to how you arrived at your solution.

Debriefing Guide

- What factors did you have to consider in marking your stick?
- Are your markings evenly spaced on the stick? Why or why not?
- What is the relationship between the marks on the stick and the volume in the tank?
- Would your stick work for any cylinder? Why or why not?
- Is there another size cylinder for which your stick would work?
- Would you have to dig out the same volume of dirt to bury the tank standing upright?
- How would the stick be different if the tank were standing upright?
- Which research and development team made the best recommendation? Why?

Protecting the Environment

Have you ever thought about all that is involved in getting gasoline into an automobile? When you look at a gas station or service station, you never see the storage tanks. That's because they are buried underground. Recently, the Environmental Protection Agency (EPA) found that many of these underground storage tanks are letting the gasoline seep out. As a result, some stations are having to have the tanks dug up and replaced with new ones. This expense is putting many small stations out of business. Has this happened in your area? How can you find out?

Contact a local gas or service station and find out the following.
- How has the EPA's ruling affected their station?
- How do they determine if a tank is leaking?
- What is the hazard if the tank is leaking?
- What is involved in replacing leaking tanks?
- Do they use a calibrated stick to determine how much gas remains in their tanks?

Write a one-page narrative describing the problem and its effect on the station you researched.

Can the Idea

America's soft drink companies have been trying to establish good public relations by using aluminum cans and encouraging people to recycle them. It has been brought to their attention, however, that if they were truly interested in best utilizing America's resources, they would restructure the soft drink can.

Unbelievable! Could it be possible to make a more efficient soda can? The soft drink companies of America have decided to hire an outside agency to investigate this and present their findings.

Your company has been asked to investigate the soft drink can problem. The soft drink companies want to know if the current can is really the most efficient way to package their soft drinks. Your company's task is to investigate the relationship between the surface area of the can and its volume. You want to know if it would be possible to make a cylinder that uses less aluminum, but holds the same volume of soda.

After your company has investigated the problem, your task, as the executive vice-president, is to present your company's findings in the form of a report that includes a recommendation based on the findings.

Debriefing Guide

- What is the surface area of the can?
- What is the volume of the can?
- Were you able to design a better can? If so, what are its dimensions?
- What other factors need to be taken into consideration before changing the can size?
- What conclusions can you draw?

What Size Can?

Have you ever thought about the different-sized cans in which items are packaged? Do you think that the size of the can is always the most efficient?

Find three items in your home that are in cans. Calculate the volume and surface area of each can.

Select one of the cans and redesign it so that the same contents are contained in a can with the same volume, but less surface area.

Which has the greater impact on volume, an increase in the height of the can or an increase in the radius of the base?

What factors do you think manufacturers consider when designing packaging for their products?

SELECTION AND REFLECTION

What have you learned about surface area and volume while studying this unit? What was your favorite activity in this unit? Gather together the papers or the work you did in your favorite activity. Explain what the activity was about and why you liked it. Was there anything you studied in this unit that you still feel you don't understand? Was there anything you didn't study in this unit that you wish you had?

The Problem

Mr. Jackson owns a plot of land in the shape of a trapezoid, as shown below. He plans to give half of the land to his son, Ben, as a wedding present. Where should the boundary line be placed so that Mr. Jackson and Ben get equal-sized plots?

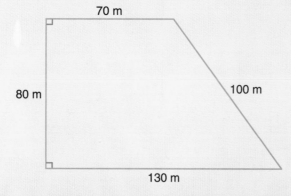

70 m

80 m

100 m

130 m

THE GREAT DIVIDE

Fold or Be Fooled

The Problem

Five squares were used to form each of the pentominoes shown below. Which of these figures can be folded into an open-top box? (Only fold on the dashed lines.)

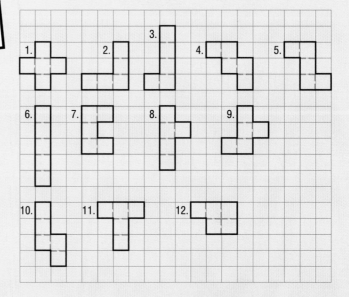

The Problem

A Tight Fit

Imagine that there are five rectangles where the measure of the length and width of each rectangle is a whole number from 1 to 10, and that you can only use each number once. Now imagine that these five rectangles can be fit together to form a square, with no spaces between the rectangles. Draw a sketch of this square, showing how each rectangle fits.

Don't Be So Dense

The Problem

In physics class, Mike accidently drops a sugar cube into the graduated cylinder shown below. If the sugar cube is $\frac{1}{2}$ inch on a side and has a mass of 3.2 grams, where would it end up in the graduated cylinder? (Assume that the sugar cube will not dissolve.)

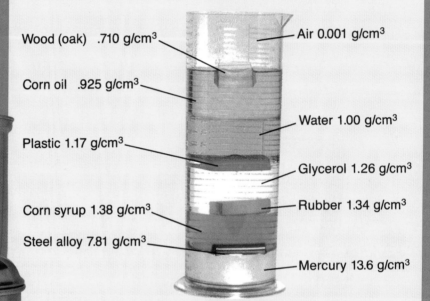

Wood (oak) .710 g/cm³

Air 0.001 g/cm³

Corn oil .925 g/cm³

Water 1.00 g/cm³

Plastic 1.17 g/cm³

Glycerol 1.26 g/cm³

Corn syrup 1.38 g/cm³

Rubber 1.34 g/cm³

Steel alloy 7.81 g/cm³

Mercury 13.6 g/cm³

Extension Use the Densities of Common Materials table in the Data Bank to find out where ethanol, blood, and copper would fall in the graduated cylinder shown above.

The Problem

Each square below is 6 units long on a side. Find the area of the circle inscribed in the first square and the sum of the areas of the circles inscribed in the other two squares. Which square contains the greatest area covered by circles? What is that area?

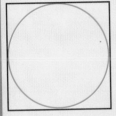 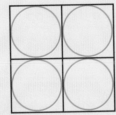 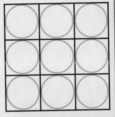

Extension Predict the sum of the areas of the circles inscribed in the squares below.

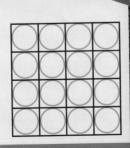

The Problem

José goes to a friend's birthday party where a magician is putting on a show. The magician holds up a Greek cross like the one shown below and says, "For my next trick, I will change this cross into a square with two straight cuts." José politely responds, "That's not magic—I can do that, too!" and proceeds to change the Greek cross into a square by dividing the cross into four pieces with two straight cuts. How did José do it?

TABLE OF CONTENTS

Landmark	Number of Steps
Wrigley Field, Chicago	67
Louisiana Superdome, New Orleans	80
Lombard Street, San Francisco	305
Statue of Liberty, New York	354
Space Needle, Seattle	832
Washington Monument, Washington	897
Gateway Arch, St. Louis	1,116
Eiffel Tower, Paris	1,652
Sears Tower, Chicago	1,707
World Trade Center, New York	1,760
Mount Katahdin, Maine	9,030
Mauna Kea, Hawaii	23,604
Mt. Kilimanjaro, Tanzania	33,154
Mt. Everest, Nepal	49,762

Note: Each step is approximately 7 inches high.

Source: *The Universal Almanac*

Date	Event
1783	Jean Pilâtre de Rozier made the **first human balloon flight** on Nov. 21, reaching a peak altitude of about 500 feet.
1784	Madame Thible, a French opera singer, was the **first woman to fly**.
1797	André-Jacques Garnerin made the **first parachute jump** in a 23-foot diameter parachute made of white canvas with a basket attached.
1903	Orville Wright made the **first successful airplane flight** on Dec. 17.
1927	Charles Lindbergh made the **first solo, nonstop transatlantic flight** in the *Spirit of St. Louis* on May 20 and 21.
1932	Ruth Rowland Nichols became the **first female airline pilot**. She also was the first woman to hold three international records at the same time—speed, distance, and altitude.
1937	Hanna Reitsch, a German pilot, flew the **first successful helicopter**.
1947	U.S. Air Force captain Charles Yeager made the **first piloted supersonic flight in an airplane**, flying faster than the speed of sound on Oct. 14.
1958	National Airlines inaugurated the **first domestic jet passenger service** between New York and Miami on Dec. 10.
1977	Paul MacCready created and flew the **first successful man-powered aircraft**, *The Gossamer Condor,* on Aug. 23.
1980	Janice Brown made the **first long-distance solar-powered flight** in the *Solar Challenger* on Dec. 3.
1986	Dick Rutan and Jeana Yeager made the **first nonstop flight around the world without refueling** in *Voyager* on December 14–23.
1993	Victoria VanMeter, at 11 years old, became the youngest female pilot ever to fly across the continental United States.

Source: *1993 Information Please Almanac*

Material	Density (g/cm^3)
natural gas	0.0006
air	0.001
ethanol	0.79
water	1.00
blood	1.06
glycerol	1.26
rubber	1.34
corn syrup	1.38
table sugar	1.59
table salt	2.16
stainless steel	7.86
copper	8.92
mercury	13.59

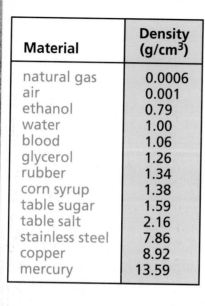
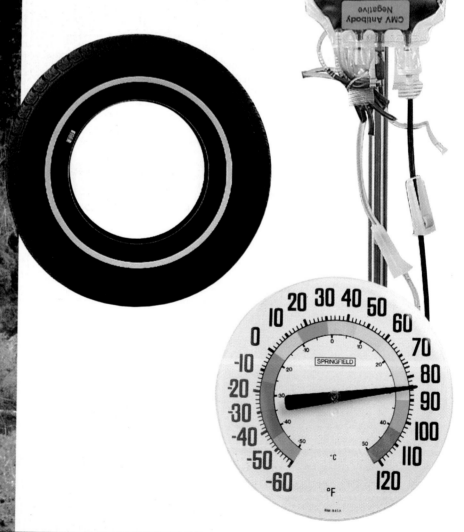

Type of Vehicle	Cars	Motorcycles	Buses	Total
Total travel (in millions of miles)	1,515,370	9,572	5,728	1,530,670
Number of registered vehicles	143,549,627	4,259,462	626,987	148,436,076
Average miles traveled per vehicle	10,556	2,247	9,136	21,939
Fuel consumed (in thousands of gallons)	72,434,884	191,440	900,629	73,526,953
Avg. fuel consumption per vehicle (in gallons)	505	45	1,436	495

Source: *1993 Information Please Almanac*

GLOSSARY INDEX

A

Acute triangle, 13

Algebra
  conversion factor, 18, 19
  ordering, 12
  plot, 37

Amount, 21

Analysis, 14

Approximate, 44

Archimedes' principle, 8, 24

Area, 7, 13, 14, 41

Average, 47

B

Base, 35

Between, 39, 40

Bivariate data, 20 data that
  uses two variables

Bottom, 6

C

Calculate, 23, 29, 35

Calculator, 10

Calibrated, 30, 32

Center, 5

Centimeter ruler, 18, 19

Centimeters, 10, 15, 16, 27, 29

Chart, 27, 29

Circle, 5, 41

Columns, 29

Combination, 20

Computer, 29

Conclusions, 12, 21, 23

Conversion factor, 18, 19

Corner, 27, 29

Cubes, 15, 16, 17, 21, 22, 25,
  26, 40

Cubic centimeters, 10, 18, 19,
  22, 29, 40, 46

Cubic meters, 7, 10

Cubic units, 12

Cylinders, 12, 19, 21, 30, 31,
  33, 40

D

Data
  bank, 40, 43, 44, 45, 46, 47

Day, 11

Density, 9, 24, 40, 46

Design, 15, 17

Diameter, 4, 5, 30

Dimensions, 27, 28, 34

Distance, 5

Divide, 6, 42

Dynes, 22

E

Equal, 9

Equal-sized plots, 37

Estimate, 7, 18, 19

Experiment, 12, 21, 27

F

Folded, 38

Formula, 15, 16, 29

G

Gallons, 47

Geometry
  acute triangle, 13
  area, 7, 13, 14, 41
  base, 35
  center, 5
  circle, 5, 41
  cylinders, 12, 19, 21, 30, 31,
    33, 40
  diameter, 4, 5, 30
  distance, 5
  formula, 15, 16, 29,
  height, 29, 35
  inscribed, 41
  length, 29, 39
  lines, 38

obtuse triangle, 13
parallelogram, 13
radius, 35
rectangle, 13, 39
rectangular prisms, 12
right triangles, 13
sphere, 5
square, 10, 29, 38, 39, 41, 42
surface area, 4, 5, 6, 7, **12,**
  14, 17, 20, 33, 34, 35, 36
three-dimensional, 5, 14
trapezoid, 13, 37
volume, 5, 6, 7, 10, **12,** 15,
  16, 17, 18, 19, 21, 22, 25,
  28, 29, 30, 31, 33, 34, 35,
  36
width, 29, 39

Graduated cylinder, 21, 22

Grams, 22, 40, 46

Greatest, 12

Greatest hang time, 20

H

Height, 29, 35

I

Inches, 26, 40, 44

Increase, 35

Inscribed, 41

Investigate, 30

L

Least, 12

Length, 29, 39

Lines, 38

M

Mass, 22, 23, 40 the amount
  of matter in an object

Mathematics toolkit, 4-11

Measurement, 6, 7, 10, 13, 18,
  19, 21, 25, 39
  age, 2

ACKNOWLEDGMENTS

4-11, From *James and the Giant Peach* by Roald Dahl. Copyright 1961 by Roald Dahl. Copyright renewed 1989 by Roald Dahl and Alfred A. Knopf, Inc. Reprinted by permission of Alfred A. Knopf, Inc.